Junior Puzzle Travel Pad

© 2003 Alligator Books Limited

Published by
Alligator Books Limited
Gadd House, Arcadia Avenue
London N3 2JU

Printed in China. 10664

HOLIDAY MESSAGE

Can you work out what the girl is saying?

IH EREHT, DNA EMOCLEW OT A LAICEPS REMMUS YADILOH NOITIDE FO ROINUJ ELZZUP NUF!

Can you name the creatures?

PIZZA EXPRESS

Can you help Dino through the maze to reach the pizza?

3

Join the Dots

Starting at No. 1, take your pencil and connect
all the dots to make a secret picture.

SPOT THE DIFFERENCE
Q ♥

There are ten differences between the two pictures. Can you spot them?

Can you complete the puzzle by entering the numbered items into the grid?

6

ACROSS

1. Disappear slowly (4)
3. Stately long-necked bird (4)
6. Mineral excavation (4)
7. Hot dish (4)
9. Country (7)
12. Leave out (4)
13. Stitch a hole up (4)
14. Small (4)
15. Sluggish (4)

DOWN

1. Popularity (4)
2. Bright yellow flower (9)
4. Cascade (9)
5. Tailed amphibian (4)
8. Large Australian bird (3)
10. Farm animal (4)
11. Winter weather (4)

1... 2...3... 4...5...

How many boxes are there in the stack?

7

TRUNK CALL

Which numbered shape will fit into 'A'?

STUDY THE PICTURE BELOW
AND SEE HOW MANY
WORDS YOU CAN FIND
HIDDEN IN THE DIAGRAM.
THE CIRCLED NUMBERS
TELL YOU HOW MANY
LETTERS IN EACH WORD.

P	A	L	M	T	R	E	E
S	C	L	P	S	U	N	S
R	H	E	B	E	A	C	H
E	A	H	W	A	S	K	O
W	I	S	A	R	O	R	R
O	R	D	R	I	N	K	T
L	O	V	T	T	I	G	S
F	S	W	S	Y	D	M	B

9

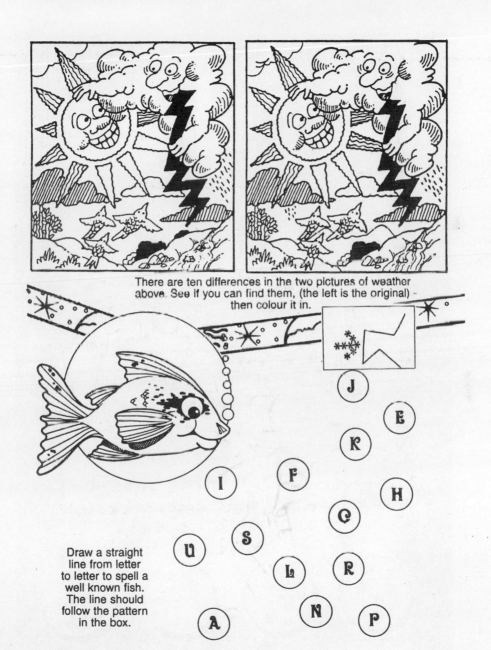

There are ten differences in the two pictures of weather above. See if you can find them, (the left is the original) then colour it in.

Draw a straight line from letter to letter to spell a well known fish. The line should follow the pattern in the box.

Re-arrange the letters below, to spell out four words associated with the picture above!

A   B   C   D

HORSE SENSE

Which piece will complete the jigsaw?

Power Words

Find the words below:

MACHINERY   SOLAR
MINERALS   STEAM
OIL   WAVES
PETROL   WIND
POWER

COAL
COOL
ELECTRICITY
ENERGY
FIRE
GAS
HEAT

```
E K M A C H I N E R Y T
C N V I S T E A M O P L
O B E E T Q P O W E R N
O I V R M I N E R A L S
L A L K G P E T R O L I
W I N D A Y F H E A T Z
F I R E S Z B S O L A R
E L E C T R I C I T Y K
```

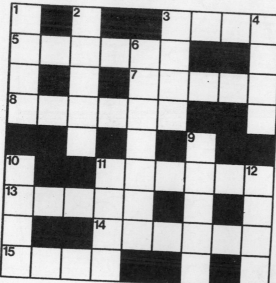

ACROSS
3. Slightly wet (4)
5. Hit (6)
7. Asian country (5)
8. One appointed to act for another (6)
11. Protection (6)
13. Boat propelled by a paddle (5)
14. Scotland's patron saint (6)
15. File (4)

DOWN
1. Employed (4)
2. Fruit of the vine (5)
3. Reject (4)
4. Theatre production (4)
6. Cooking room (7)
9. Carry over water (5)
10. Blemish (4)
11. Washing aid (4)
12. Soft feathers (4)

14

MILK SHAKER

E T A L O C O H C O T N A R R
U
C
K
N A R R E G N A R O L B L A C
A
N
A B L A K R U C H E R R Y O
S
T
L I N A V Y R E S Y R R E B W A R
A
B

See if you can spell out the following flavours of milkshakes, hidden in the bubble chain:

STRAWBERRY
BANANA
CHERRY
BLACK CURRANT

CHOCOLATE
ORANGE
VANILLA

15

```
N E G A T I V E S A T B
S C E F G A C H I H J P
U H K K R L M O G P N H
B O U E O B Q I L R S O
J C M T M U L S H O R T
E A L L T M T S C C U O
C U I O B E A V W E X R
T F Y Y U L R Z A S N B
S C S D F D E F K S L E
D A R K R O O M L E N S
```

Pick out these photo words listed below:

ALBUM   SCENE
CAMERA   SHUTTER
CLOUD   SUBJECTS
COLOUR   SUN
DARKROOM
FILM
FLASH
LENS
LIGHT
NEGATIVES
PHOTO
PROCESS

Which one of these boys is the odd one out?

COLOUR IN

Bathing Beauty

Can you find the six pairs of identical squares?

This boy was wading in the sea, but got a painful surprise when a... attacked him. If you draw a line from No. 1 to No. 2 and so on to No. 55 you'll discover what is hidden in the illustration.

Can you identify the six silhouettes?

1. Pencwen	4. Seal
2. Ant	5. Swan
3. Pelupon	6. Frog

20

H Block

Can you fill in the missing letters, helped by the clues? The Hs are already there.

1. Place to live
2. Play unfairly
3. Remains of a fire
4. Number of sides of an octagon
5. A fruit

H			
	H		
		H	
			H
				H

Can you find all the animals in the wordsearch?

Animal Collection

ALLIGATOR
CAMEL
ELEPHANT
HIPPO
MONKEY
PANDA
PARROT
RHINO
SNAKE
ZEBRA

```
Y A L G S P I H O
E L I L N A T A R
K L E M A C R N H
N I E A K B U T I
O G K P E C M O N
M A L Z H I P P O
S T U L E A B A T
C O V U N B N R H
O R M D A R N T E
G P A R R O T U R
```

DOUBLE UP

Which two slithering burping things are twins?

LINK UP

Link the words on the left with the words on the right to make eight longer words.

PAPER	ONE
BACK	LACE
STALE	HOLD
BOOT	BACK
SOME	WARDS
HOUSE	COME
HAT	MATE
OVER	RED

OPPOSITES

Each word is an antonym of another word which will fit around the central letters. (e.g. BAD ...... GOOD)

1. Narrow
2. Morning
3. Early
4. Old
5. Blush
6. Beautiful
7. Discord
8. Question

1.			A		
2.			N		
3.			T		
4.			O		
5.			N		
6.			Y		
7.			M		
8.			S		

POT LUCK

Help the bee through the maze to get to the pot of jam.

JAM

SUN
RAIN
WET
WINDY
SHOWERS
MIST
FOG
THUNDER
LIGHTENING
TORNADO

HURRICANE
HAILSTONES
SNOWSTORM
CLOUD

Under the Weather

Find the following weather words in the wordsearch.

Spot six differences in the bottom picture of Robbie.

The picture of Tina at the top left of the page is complete.
Circle what is missing from each of the other 7 pics.

CALCULATING

GRAB YOUR CALCULATORS KIDS!
AND TRY THIS CALCULATOR PUZZLE!
IF YOU TURN YOURS UP SIDE DOWN
YOU'LL NOTICE SOME NUMBERS
LOOK LIKE LETTERS. NOW LOOK
AT THE CLUES BELOW, ANSWER
THE SUMS, TURN YOUR CALCULATOR
UP SIDE DOWN AND THERE
ARE THE ANSWERS TO
THE CLUES!

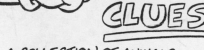

1 A COLLECTION OF ANIMALS
   $1.62 \div 81 =$

2 PLANTS GROW IN THIS
   $1421 \times 5 =$

3 SHOES MUST BE THE CORRECT ONE
   $1890 + 1325 =$

4 MUSICAL INSTRUMENT
   $9170 - 6090 =$

5 SHINY PAINT
   $13769 \times 4 =$

6 FARMYARD BIRDS
   $29384 + 5952 =$

7 GRAB
   $45714 - 13579 =$

8 TURKEY NOISE
   $3409254 \div 9 =$

ODD DUCK

Which one is the odd one out?

TRIANGULAR

Fill in only the ▲ triangles and you will see a hidden picture.

WHAT'S WRONG?

There are seven mistakes in this picture, can you find them all?

Find these words hidden below . . .

ART
CREATE
DESIGN
DRAW
DREAM

EXPRESSION
IDEAS
IMAGINATION
PAINT
SKETCH

```
I M A G I N A T I O N K
R D O N M L T P D R A W
S B E A I T O E A R T O
C R E A T E D E S I G N
T R A I S K E T C H N O
D E X P R E S S I O N T
```

Which watch face is
the odd-one out?

35

SPOT THE DIFFERENCE

Spot ten differences between the two pictures.

36

24 + 71 =	2951**5**
11 − 6 =	526**5**42
44 + 21 =	86**65**23
83 − 30 =	240**53**0
92 − 21 =	952**71**1
50 + 22 =	47**72**62
24 + 33 =	571**57**431
95 + 8 =	7**103**02
72 − 10 =	7**62**1621

Solve the arithmetic problem on the left and then find the
answer to the problem hidden in the number on the right.

Sun Stroke

Here's a real **SUN HAT**! Can you change **SUN** to **HAT** in four moves, by changing one letter at a time?

Pair the words
which are
opposites.

LARGE
DIRTY
ENTRANCE
SQUARE
CEILING
EARLY
LAUGH
LATE
LAND
CIRCLE
DRY
SEA
CLEAN
SMALL
WET
FLOOR
CRY
EXIT

ASTER
AZALEAS
DAHLIA
DAISIES
ELMS
GLAD
GRASS
IVY
LILIES
PEAS
RADISH
ROSES
SAGE
TREES
TULIPS
VIOLET

S A E L A Z A Y
S E S O R Y S V
A J E P L E T I
R I I R I L E O
G P L S T L R L
L E I H M N U E
A A L S A G E T
D S H S I D A R

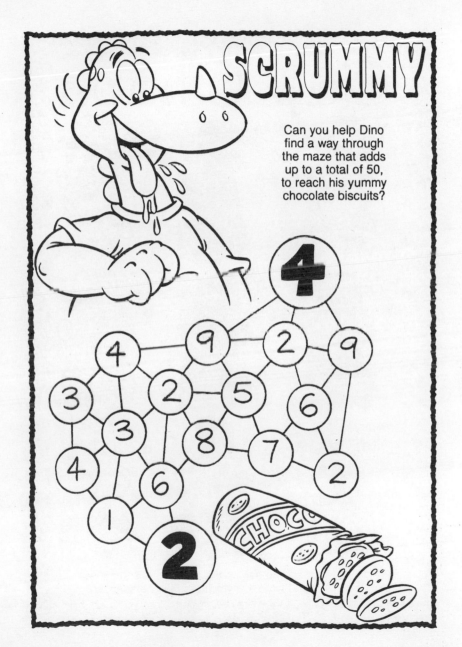

SCRUMMY

Can you help Dino find a way through the maze that adds up to a total of 50, to reach his yummy chocolate biscuits?

Cap Chaps

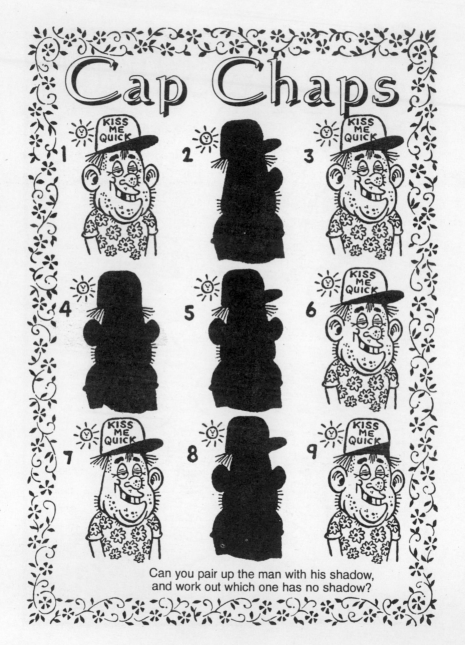

Can you pair up the man with his shadow, and work out which one has no shadow?

SHARK INFESTED

Which shark is
the odd one out?

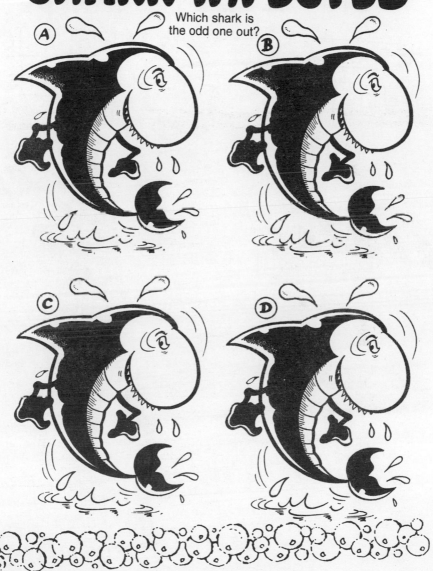

COMPLETE THE WORDS

① T O [ ] [ ] [ ]

② T O [ ] [ ]

③ T O [ ] [ ]

④ T O [ ] [ ]

⑤ T O [ ] [ ]

Fill in the missing letters using the drawings as clues.

Use the code to read the names of animals found in a zoo.

A	B	C	D	E	F	G	H	I	J	K	L	M

N	O	P	Q	R	S	T	U	V	W	X	Y	Z

Using the pictures as clues fill in the
grid and discover the summer words
hidden in the circles.

Bird Watcher

Rearrange the letters to find the names of birds.

1 NETNAG	10 ARDZZUB
2 ANTPHEAS	11 OROMNEH
3 GAPWILN	12 FACHCHINF
4 LOWLAWS	13 GLODCHINF
5 SLAKRYK	14 LINGRATS
6 MEGAPI	15 WACKJAD
7 VENRA	16 GWAXWIN
8 WERN	17 BORNI
9 DACKBRILB	18 FEENGRINCH

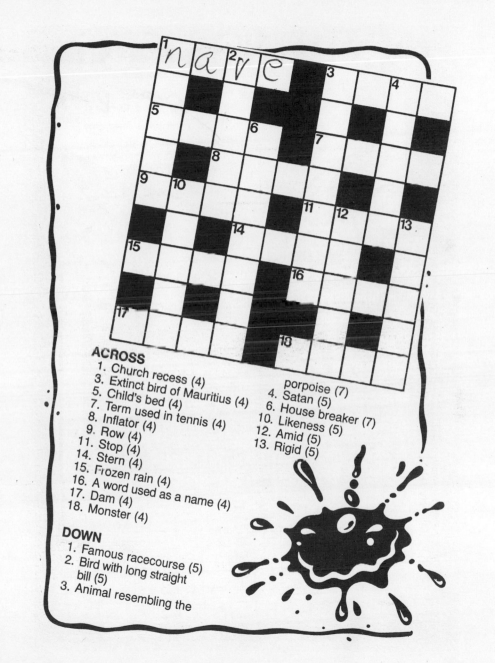

ACROSS

1. Church recess (4)
3. Extinct bird of Mauritius (4)
5. Child's bed (4)
7. Term used in tennis (4)
8. Inflator (4)
9. Row (4)
11. Stop (4)
14. Stern (4)
15. Frozen rain (4)
16. A word used as a name (4)
17. Dam (4)
18. Monster (4)

porpoise (7)
4. Satan (5)
6. House breaker (7)
10. Likeness (5)
12. Amid (5)
13. Rigid (5)

DOWN

1. Famous racecourse (5)
2. Bird with long straight bill (5)
3. Animal resembling the

DRIVING TEST

Find the words hidden in the puzzle.

1 CLUTCH   2 BONNET

3 LIGHTS

4 ALTERNATOR

5 BOOT   6 DOORS

7 BRAKES

8 ROOF

9 CAMSHAFT

11 SEATS   10 PLUGS

B	L	T	A	R	O	T	A	N	R	E	T	L	A
A	S	B	F	L	S	T	H	G	I	L	C	S	L
S	G	H	S	A	L	B	L	F	C	R	A	B	T
E	U	C	A	L	H	S	R	O	O	D	B	A	E
K	L	T	C	R	B	S	L	A	L	O	S	L	N
A	P	U	L	A	S	L	M	T	B	C	R	A	N
R	A	L	L	D	B	S	T	A	E	S	S	L	O
B	E	C	S	C	L	R	L	B	C	T	O	O	B

ACROSS

3. Agricultural establishment (4)
5. Car service station (6)
7. Roof room (5)
8. On fire (6)
11. Powerless plane (6)
13. Test (5)
14. Discharge (3,3)
15. Metal thread (4)

DOWN

1. Indian city (4)
2. Boring instrument (5)
3. Festival (4)
4. Metal-headed war club (4)
6. Small antelope (7)
9. Fool (5)
10. Meat and vegetable dish (4)
11. Strong wind (4)
12. Floating structure (4)

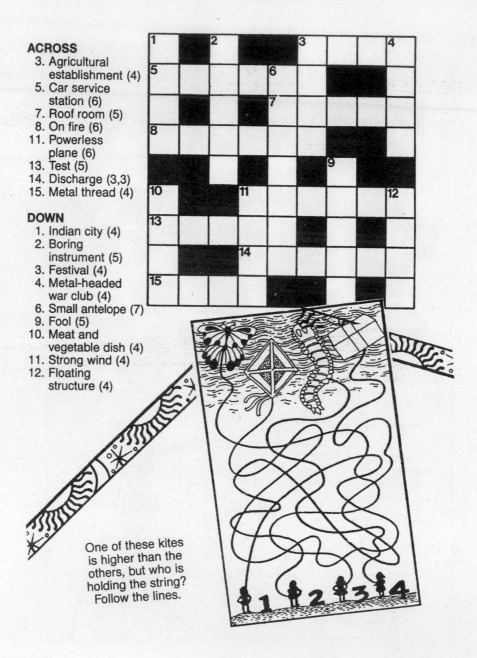

One of these kites is higher than the others, but who is holding the string? Follow the lines.

Find the surnames of 7 football players in the ball chain.

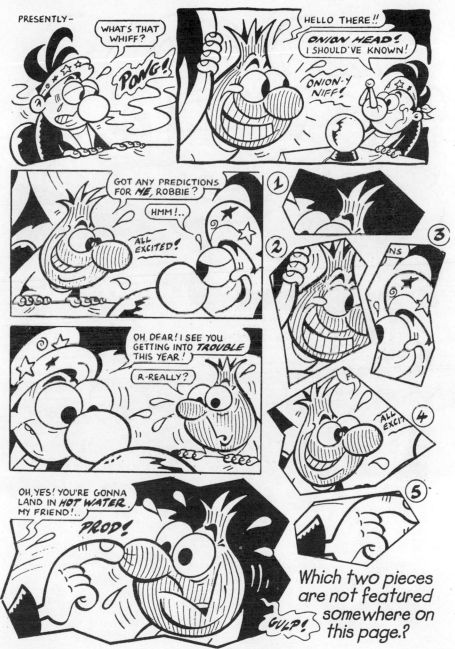

Editor's note: I predict loadsa laffs in Qwizzer throughout the year. And I should know – 'cos I'm the editor!

56

Mmmmmm Words

Can you fill in the missing letters in the following words with the help of the clues?

1. M _ M M _   Mother
2. M _ M M _ _   Warm-blooded creature
3. M _ M _ _ _   We use this to remember things
4. M _ _ _ M̄ _ M   The most
5. M _ _ _ M _ M̄   The least
6. _ M̄ M _ _   Season with most sunshine
7. M̄ _ M _ _   Disease with swollen glands

School journey

Can you help Laura through the maze to reach her school things?

MATHS BOOK

58

Frozen Treats

```
S C M C S N A E B D A O R B L
W P A A I A Z Z I P S A S P A
U S I C E C U B E S N O B G M
E A O H A R O S T I U C S I B
C R E K C X C R A P B W L I K E
A H E T E H A E Q G D E L P C Y
R S I S A T E T C T E T O A C Y
T H S C T G V E O I K S R S S
O P T I K L I M S J O R L E E
N O U D S E A O F E O X V I P
O R O B N T N M B T C A F P O
F K R E O U Z R S E O A H T C
L I P E C S A E P L A E K A S
A N S F A D B H M R U N N E R
N G T H B C I T S A L P S M A
```

BACON
BEEF
BISCUITS
BROAD BEANS
BUNS
CAKES
CARROTS
CARTON
 OF/MILK
CHEESECAKE
CHICKEN
CHIPS

COOKED/
 TOMATOES
FISH
FLAN/CASE
FRUIT TARTS
GATEAU
ICE CREAM
ICE CUBES
LAMB
LOAVES
MEAT PIES
PEAS

PIZZA
PLASTIC/BOXES
PORK
ROLLS
RUNNER/BEANS
SAUSAGES
SCONES
SOUP
SPROUTS
STEW
THERMOMETER

First Aid

This poor bandaged man just fell on his head! Can you change FELL to HEAD in three moves, by changing one letter at a time?

Can you spot 6 differences
between the two pictures?

Take the first letter of each object to spell out something found in a haunted house!

Can you find these haunted house words in the wordsearch?

```
Y L B H U T G T O D S I R
L O I A I S H R L N K D I
I N T B O M O N S T E R S
R H K C L O S D P O L B S
Y O N H I T T V I E E N T
P U W A I L S W D A T U M
A U R E I A K N D E U O R A
M O A N S N O O R T N E L
H E U S I A N E S A S Y N
```

GHOSTS
CHAINS
MOANS
MONSTERS
SKELETONS
SPIDERS
WAILS

Cold Comfort

Which two pieces are not part of
the picture of the coughing boy?

LOST IN SPACE

Alien ZARG is looking at a photo of his solar system.
Find a pathway to lead him back to his planet
"THWONK" (No crossing any lines, remember!)

PLANETARY

SNOOZE VIEWS

Which two pictures of the sleeping dog are identical?

SEASIDER

Find the hidden letters, then rearrange
to spell a well-known holiday resort.

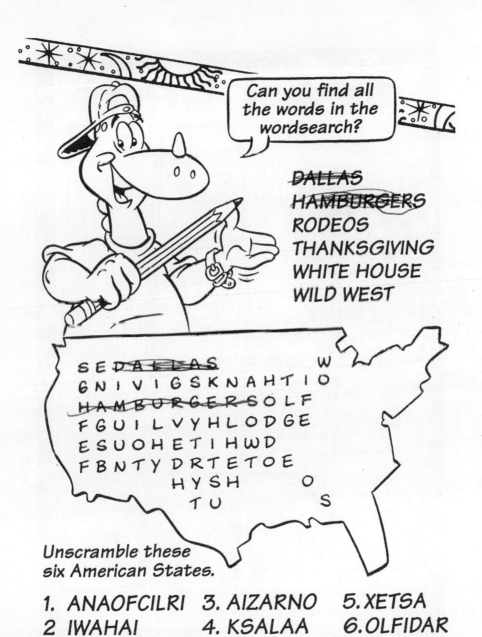

Can you find all the words in the wordsearch?

DALLAS
HAMBURGERS
RODEOS
THANKSGIVING
WHITE HOUSE
WILD WEST

S E D A L L A S W
G N I V I G S K N A H T I O
H A M B U R G E R S O L F
F G U I L V Y H L O D G E
E S U O H E T I H W D
F B N T Y D R T E T O E
H Y S H O
T U S

Unscramble these six American States.

1. ANAOFCILRI 3. AIZARNO 5. XETSA
2 IWAHAI 4. KSALAA 6. OLFIDAR

Least Leaf

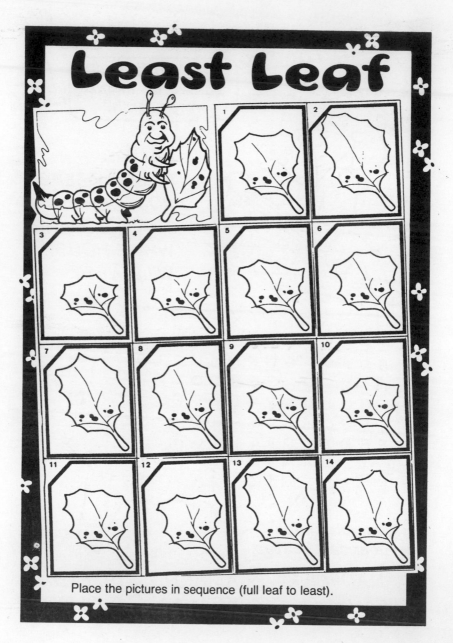

Place the pictures in sequence (full leaf to least).

73

COLOUR-IN

Memorise

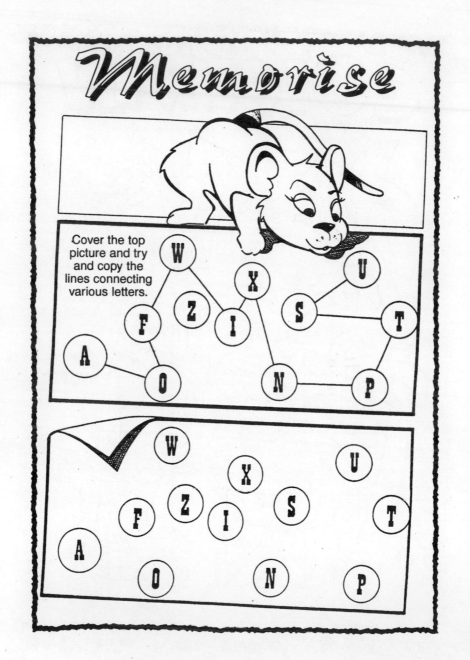

Cover the top picture and try and copy the lines connecting various letters.

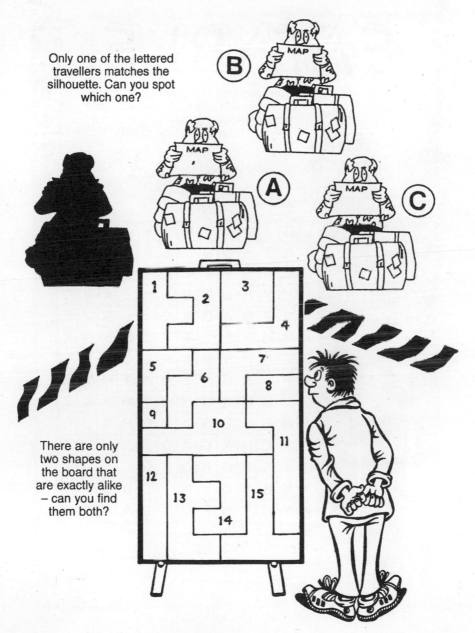

Only one of the lettered travellers matches the silhouette. Can you spot which one?

B

A

C

There are only two shapes on the board that are exactly alike – can you find them both?

MAP

1
2
3
4
5
6
7
8
9
10
11
12
13
14
15

EATABLE

Colour in only the boxes that contain
the letters DACHSHUND and you'll find
a trick (another name for dachshund)
and treat (something to eat).

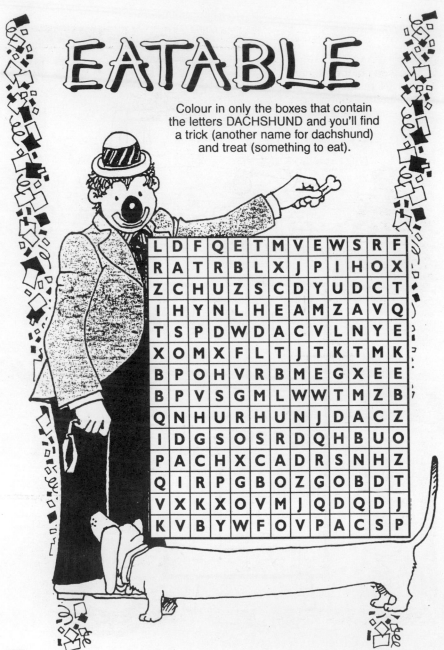

L	D	F	Q	E	T	M	V	E	W	S	R	F
R	A	T	R	B	L	X	J	P	I	H	O	X
Z	C	H	U	Z	S	C	D	Y	U	D	C	T
I	H	Y	N	L	H	E	A	M	Z	A	V	Q
T	S	P	D	W	D	A	C	V	L	N	Y	E
X	O	M	X	F	L	T	J	T	K	T	M	K
B	P	O	H	V	R	B	M	E	G	X	E	E
B	P	V	S	G	M	L	W	W	T	M	Z	B
Q	N	H	U	R	H	U	N	J	D	A	C	Z
I	D	G	S	O	S	R	D	Q	H	B	U	O
P	A	C	H	X	C	A	D	R	S	N	H	Z
Q	I	R	P	G	B	O	Z	G	O	B	D	T
V	X	K	X	O	V	M	J	Q	D	Q	D	J
K	V	B	Y	W	F	O	V	P	A	C	S	P

JOIN THE DOTS

ACROSS

1. Right hand side of a ship (9)
5. Wealthy (4)
7. Thick string (4)
8. Deep moan (5)
11. Rod or post (4)
12. Cylindrical barrel (4)
13. Undergarment (9)

DOWN

2. Cut back (4)
3. Garden of fruit trees (7)
4. Uncommon (4)
6. Reap (7)
9. Middle part of fruit (4)
10. Musical instrument (4)

LOST DIRECTION

HELP ME TO FIND MY WAY HOME

HOME

Airport Arrivals

Superintendent Smith has gone to the airport, in search of the person who has stolen a most precious diamond. He knows for sure that the person in question:

- **doesn't wear glasses**
- **has a bag**
- **doesn't wear black shoes**
- **enjoys an excellent health**
- **does not wear a tie**

ARE YOU ABLE TO GIVE HIM A HAND IN HIS SEARCH?

81

CODEBREAKER

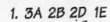

FIND WORDS IN THE GRID USING EACH OF THE SEVEN CODES!

1. 3A 2B 2D 1E
2. 1D 1B 3B 1A 2D
3. 2A 1C 3E 2E 1C 1B
4. 1A 3B 3A 3A 3D 1C
5. 2A 1C 2B 3D 3B 2C 3E
6. 3A 3D 2B 2D 1E 1C 2E
7. 2D 2B 2C 2E 3C 1D 2B 3D

	A	B	C	D	E
1	W	R	E	C	K
2	J	A	U	N	T
3	B	O	I	L	S

DOG LEADS

Which two dog pictures are identical?

A

B

C

D

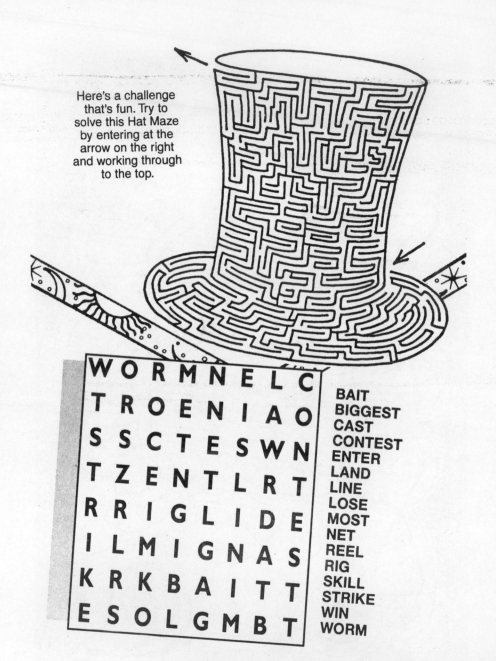

Here's a challenge that's fun. Try to solve this Hat Maze by entering at the arrow on the right and working through to the top.

```
W O R M N E L C
T R O E N I A O
S S C T E S W N
T Z E N T L R T
R R I G L I D E
I L M I G N A S
K R K B A I T T
E S O L G M B T
```

BAIT
BIGGEST
CAST
CONTEST
ENTER
LAND
LINE
LOSE
MOST
NET
REEL
RIG
SKILL
STRIKE
WIN
WORM

BEACHCOMBER

The names of twelve rock pool creatures are
spelt out hidden in the picture.

VOWEL PLAY

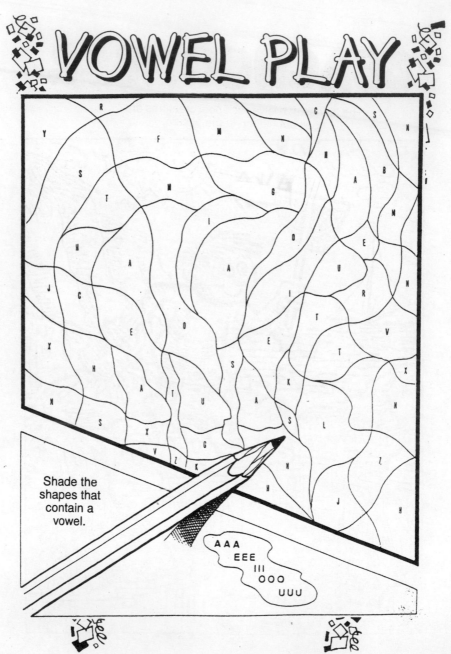

Shade the shapes that contain a vowel.

AAA
EEE
III
OOO
UUU

Heave Ho!

Which picture of the yacht is the **ODD ONE OUT**?

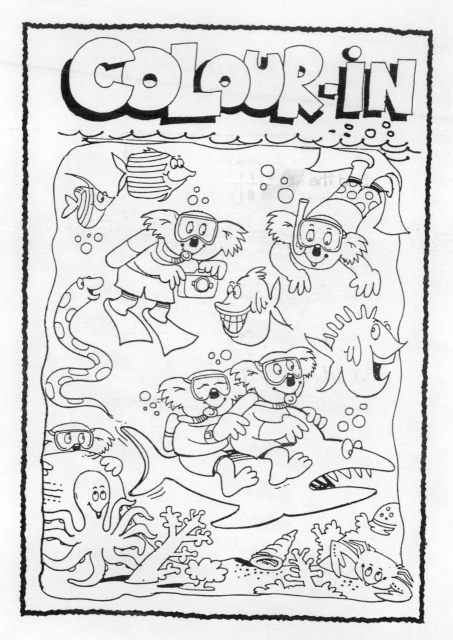

CLOTHES SHOW

Find the following words in the wordsearch

GLOVES
SOCKS
JUMPER
HAT
SHIRT
SCARF
COAT
SHOE

	A	G	D	V			
X	E	G	L	O	V	E	S	R	D
B	M	W	C	G	E	E	D
S	O	C	K	S	P	M	E
K	C	J	W	M	T	G	E
G	Z	A	U	J	E	N	T
T	J	N	T	A	H
I	P	K	R	P	N
P	H	T	I	F	T
K	C	W	H	R	P
E	O	H	S	A	Y
S	A	T	U	C	Q
T	P	E	S

90

Pencil Point

Which path will lead this girl to her pencil?

Ⓐ

Ⓑ

Ⓒ

SPOT THE DIFFERENCE

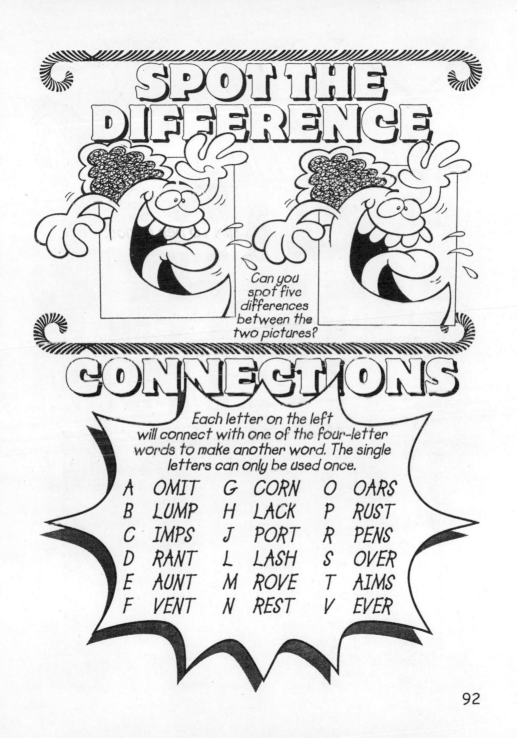

Can you spot five differences between the two pictures?

CONNECTIONS

Each letter on the left will connect with one of the four-letter words to make another word. The single letters can only be used once.

A	OMIT	G	CORN	O	OARS
B	LUMP	H	LACK	P	RUST
C	IMPS	J	PORT	R	PENS
D	RANT	L	LASH	S	OVER
E	AUNT	M	ROVE	T	AIMS
F	VENT	N	REST	V	EVER

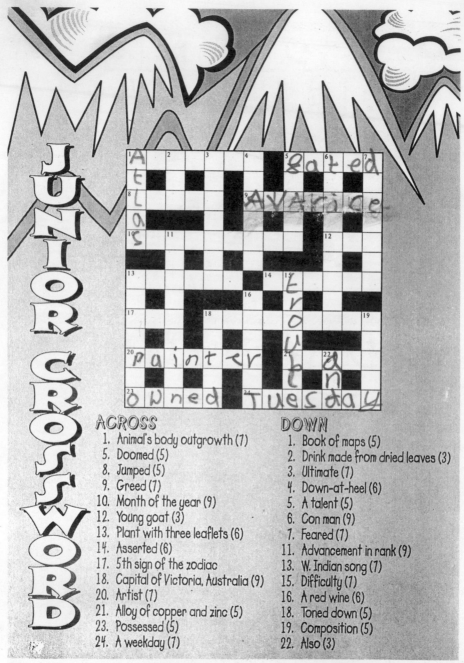

JUNIOR CROSSWORD

ACROSS
1. Animal's body outgrowth (7)
5. Doomed (5)
8. Jumped (5)
9. Greed (7)
10. Month of the year (9)
12. Young goat (3)
13. Plant with three leaflets (6)
14. Asserted (6)
17. 5th sign of the zodiac
18. Capital of Victoria, Australia (9)
20. Artist (7)
21. Alloy of copper and zinc (5)
23. Possessed (5)
24. A weekday (7)

DOWN
1. Book of maps (5)
2. Drink made from dried leaves (3)
3. Ultimate (7)
4. Down-at-heel (6)
5. A talent (5)
6. Con man (9)
7. Feared (7)
11. Advancement in rank (9)
13. W. Indian song (7)
15. Difficulty (7)
16. A red wine (6)
18. Toned down (5)
19. Composition (5)
22. Also (3)

SANDWICH FILLER
Re-arrange the letters in each case to reveal what's in Sarah's sandwich!
CLEUTET
HESECE
OTMAOT
NICKECH
MUCBERUC
SAYNOMENIA
MAH

MILK SHAKE UP

Can you help Brainwave through the maze to reach the milkshake?

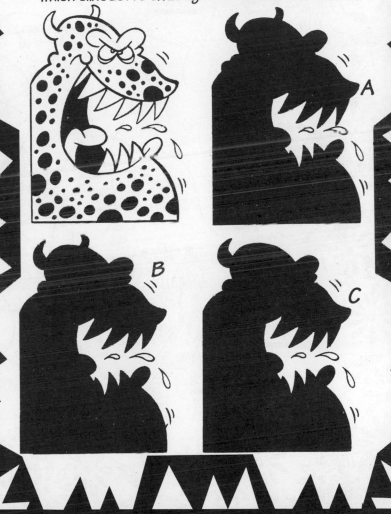

Talk

Which of Jennys friends is calling her?

Re-arrange the first letters of each object to find out where the girls are going out to

SPOT THE DIFFERENCE

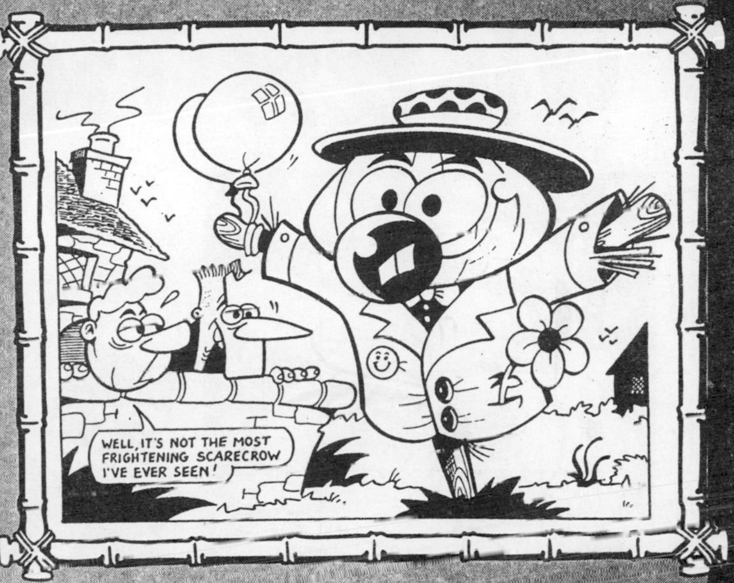

Can you spot ten differences between the two pictures?

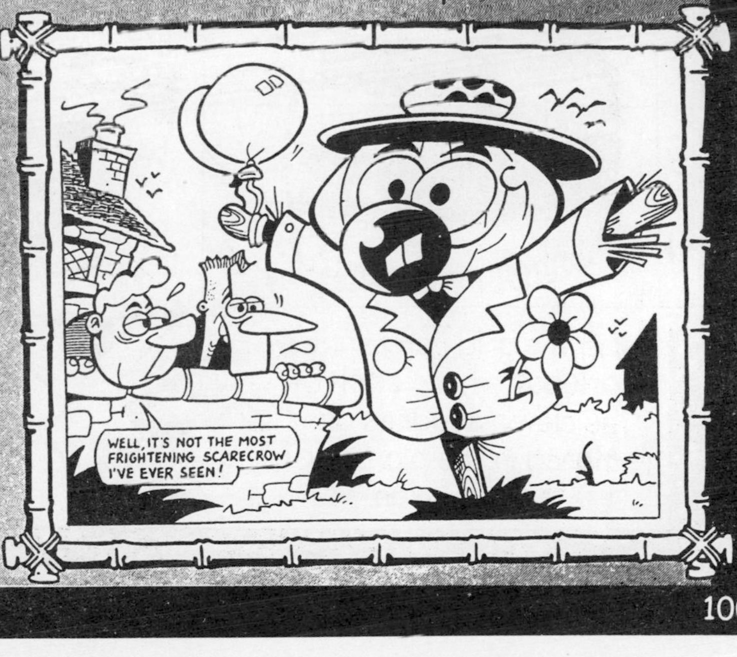

WELL, IT'S NOT THE MOST FRIGHTENING SCARECROW I'VE EVER SEEN!

100

Winters Trail

Using the grid references, work out where each of the eleven squares are featured in the picture of the snowman.

101

Serial Letters

Can you complete the series, kids?

A
E
I
U
Q
M

Odd Man Out

1.	THATCHER	REAGAN	CHURCHILL	_ _ _ _ _ _
2.	EVEREST	HIGHLANDS	PEAKS	_ _ _ _ _ _
3.	LETTUCE	RADISH	THYME	_ _ _ _ _ _
4.	SCORN	RESPECT	RUDENESS	_ _ _ _ _ _
5.	IRELAND	KENT	DEVON	_ _ _ _ _ _
6.	GROCER	ENGINEER	BAKER	_ _ _ _ _ _
7.	TIMIDITY	COWARDICE	VALOUR	_ _ _ _ _ _
8.	CEASE	END	ENDURE	_ _ _ _ _ _
9.	RHINE	THAMES	AVON	_ _ _ _ _ _

Each line of 3 words contains one that differs in some way from the other two. Write it down at the side. If correct, the first letter of each word will reveal a breed of dog.

103

POP ROUTE

Polly's just bought a CD of her favourite pop group. Can you find the right route to spell out the name of the group?

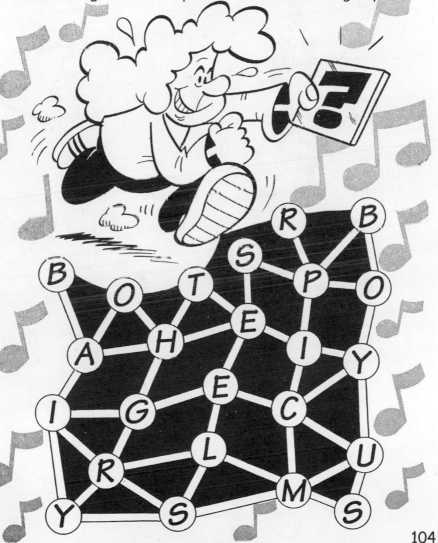

104

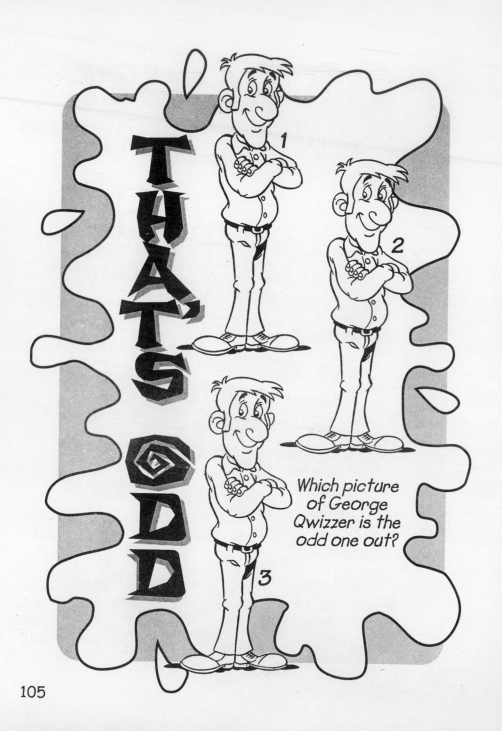

THAT'S ODD

Which picture of George Qwizzer is the odd one out?

D R I N K S

FAIR FUN

Fit the words into the grid

3 LETTERS	KIDS	GHOST	~~DRINKS~~	8 LETTERS
BUY	RIDE	MUSIC	HOOPLA	BALLOONS
FUN	SHOW	PENNY	HOT DOG	CAROUSEL
PAY		STALL		
WIN	5 LETTERS	SWING	7 LETTERS	10 LETTERS
	BINGO	TRAIN	COCONUT	AMUSEMENTS
4 LETTERS	CHUTE	WHEEL	DODGEMS	CANDY FLOSS
FAIR	CROWD		PINBALL	ROUNDABOUT
FOOD	ENJOY	6 LETTERS	WALTZER	
ICES	GAMES	ARCADE		

Cat Chorus

Re-arrange the letters that appear once to form the cats favourite type of music.

All of these kids are saying the same number in their own language, except for one who is saying a different number. Which one?

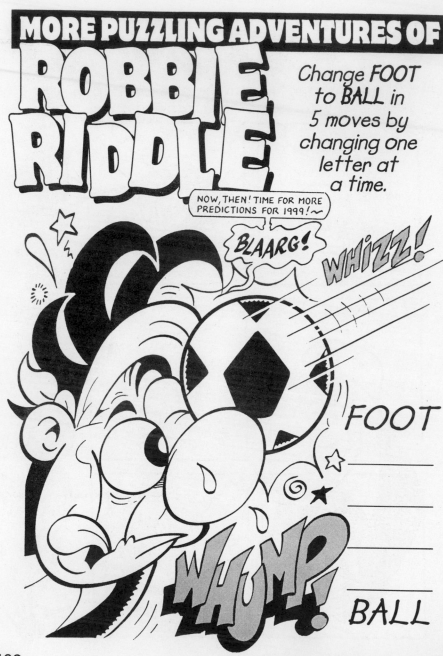

FLAVOUR FULL

Rearrange the letters in each case to spell out the names of the four different flavours in this giant ice cream.

1. NIVALAL
2. BRASTWERYR
3. ANBAAN
4. LOCHETACO

Painting by Numbers

Use the first letter of each picture clue to discover in which colours the butterfly should be printed.

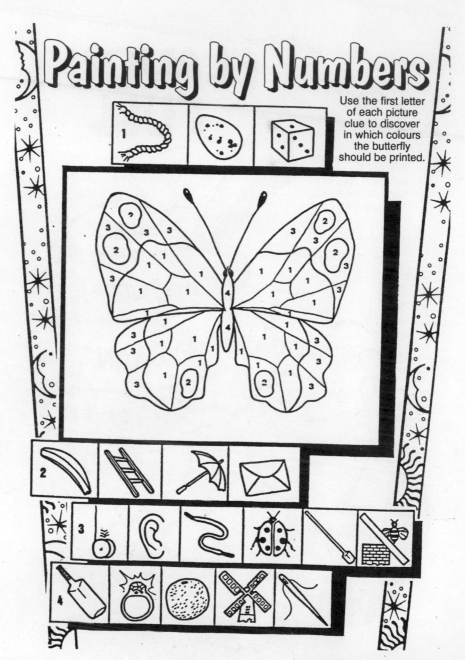

111

Can you spot five differences between the two pictures?

ACROSS

1. Colour (5)
6. Side (4)
7. Earth (4)
8. Correspondence (6)
12. European river (6)
15. Operatic song (4)
16. Employed (4)
17. Look at closely (5)

DOWN

2. House covering (4)
3. Watering place (4)
4. Open country (5)
5. Fashionable (5)
9. Flow back (3)
10. Smell (5)
11. Wrath (5)
13. Direction (4)
14. Tie up (4)

ROAD RUNNER

Find a way through the maze to collect the highest total.

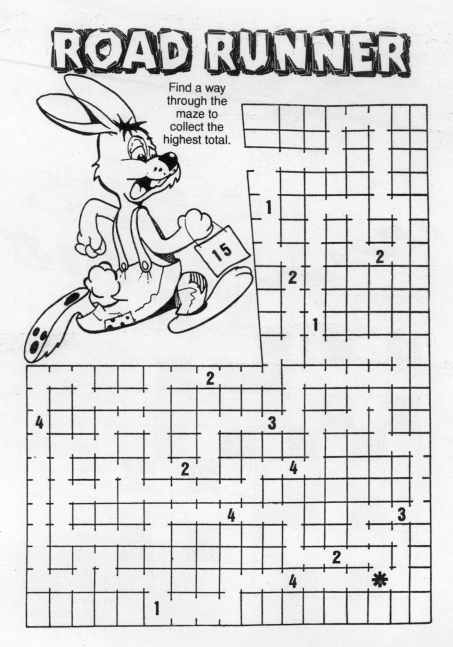

SPOT THE DIFFERENCE

Spot ten differences between the two pictures!

114

JOIN THE DOTS

Solutions

Page 1

"Hi there, and welcome to a special summer holiday edition of Junior Holiday Fun!"

Page 2

1. Whale, 2. Bat, 3. Turtle, 4. Polar Bear, 5. Seal, 6. Frog, 7. Salmon.

Page 3

Page 4

Page 5

Page 6

Page 7

Across: 1. Fade, 3. Swan, 6. Mine, 7. Stew, 9. Denmark, 12. Omit, 13. Darn, 14. Tiny, 15. Slow. Down: 1. Fame, 2. Dandelion, 4. Waterfall, 5. Newt, 8. Emu, 10. Goat, 11. Snow.

24 Boxes.

Page 8

Shape No. 2.

Page 9

Page 10

Plaice.

Solutions

Page 11

A. Starfish, B. Swimming Costume, C. Shell,
D. Ocean.

Page 12

Piece E.

Page 13

Across: 3. Damp, 5. Strike, 7. India, 8. Deputy, 11. Shield,
13. Canoe, 14. Andrew, 15. Rasp.
Down: 1. Used, 2. Grape, 3. Deny, 4. Play, 6. Kitchen, 9. Ferry,
10. Scar, 11. Soap, 12. Down.

Page 15

Page 16

Line 2.

Page 17

No. 3 is wearing one different shoe.

Page 19

A4 – E5, B2 – F4, E2 – F7, A3 – D8, A1 – C2,
E1 – C8.

Page 20

1. Pelican, 2. Ant, 3. Penguin, 4. Seal, 5. Swan,
6. Frog.

Page 21

1. House, 2. Cheat, 3. Ashes,
4. Eight, 5. Peach.

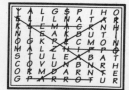

Solutions

Page 22

1 and 6.

Page 23

Paperback, Backwards, Stalemate, Bootlace, Someone, Household, Hatred, Overcome.

1. Broad, 2. Evening, 3. Late, 4. Young, 5. Blanch, 6. Ugly, 7. Harmony, 8. Answer.

Page 24

Page 25

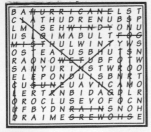

Page 26

Onion C.

Page 27

Page 28

Page 29

Orange.

Page 30

1. Zoo, 2. Soil, 3. Size, 4. Oboe, 5. Gloss, 6. Geese, 7. Seize, 8. Gobble.

Solutions

Page 31

Path A.

Page 32

No. 4.

Page 33

Page 34

Page 35

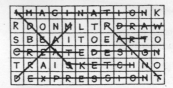

Face E. In five of them the spots are one-space-three, the sixth is two-space-two.

Page 36

Page 37

24+71=	29515
11−6=	52642
44+21=	86523
83−30=	240530
92−21=	95271
50+22=	47262
24+33=	571431
95+8=	710302
72−10=	721621

Page 38

Sun – Bun – Ban – Bat – Hat.

Solutions

Page 39

Entrance/Exit, Land/Sea, Clean/Dirty, Laugh/Cry, Small/Large, Wet/Dry, Circle/Square, Early/Late, Ceiling/Floor.

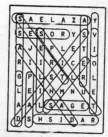

Page 40

4 – 9 6 – 7 – 8 – 2 – 4 – 3 – 4 – 1 – 2.

Page 41

1 – 8, 7 – 2, 3 – 5, 9 – 4 and 6 has no shadow.

Page 42

Shark A.

Page 43

1. Toast, 2. Toes, 3. Top, 4. Towel, 5. Toy.

Lion, Zebra, Camel, Tiger, Leopard.

Page 44

Surfboard.

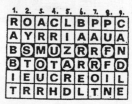

Page 45

1. Gannet, 2. Pheasant, 3. Lapwing, 4. Swallow, 5. Skylark, 6. Magpie, 7. Raven, 8. Wren, 9. Blackbird, 10. Buzzard, 11. Moorhen, 12. Chaffinch, 13. Goldfinch, 14. Starling, 15. Jackdaw, 16. Waxwing, 17. Robin, 18. Greenfinch.

Page 46

Across: 1. Apse, 3. Dodo, 5. Crib, 7. Love, 8. Pump, 9. Tier, 11. Holt, 14. Grim, 15. Hail, 16. Noun, 17. Weir, 18. Ogre.
Down: 1. Ascot, 2. Snipe, 3. Dolphin, 4. Devil, 6. Burglar, 10. Image, 12. Among, 13. Tense.

Page 47

Page 48

The square.

Page 49

Across: 3. Farm, 5. Garage, 7. Attic, 8. Ablaze, 11. Glider, 13. Trial, 14. Let off, 15. Wire.
Down: 1. Agra, 2. Drill, 3. Fete, 4. Mace, 6. Gazelle, 9. Idiot, 10. Stew, 11. Gale, 12. Raft.

Kite No. 3.

Solutions

Page 50

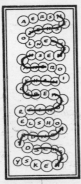

David BECKHAM, Roy KEANE, Micheal OWEN, Emile HESKEY, Colin HENDRY, David GINOLA, Mark HUGHES.

Page 51

Page 52

1 and 3.

Page 53

Silhouette 3.

Page 54

Planets 1 & 4.

Page 55

1. G1. 2. F6. 3. E2. 4. C6. 5. A4. 6. C3. 7. E4. 8. B4. 9. B2. 10. G4.

Page 57

Page 58

1. Mummy. 2. Mammal. 3. Memory. 4. Maximum. 5. Minimum. 6. Summer. 7. Mumps.

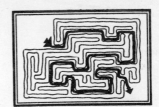

Solutions

Page 59

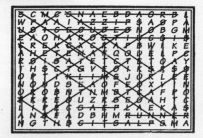

Page 60

Page 61

Werewolf.

Page 62

Fell, Hell, Heal, Head.

Page 63

Silhouette 3.

Page 64

Page 65

Witch

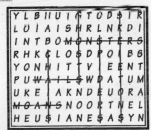

Page 66

B and F.

Page 67

10-8-12-9-11.

Page 68

Solutions

Page 69

Page 70

1 and 5.

Page 71

Brighton.

Page 72

1. California, 2. Hawaii, 3. Arizona, 4. Alaska, 5. Texas, 6. Florida.

Page 73

2, 13, 7, 14, 8, 1, 11, 6, 12, 5, 10, 4, 9 and 3.

Page 76

Traveller B.

2 and 14.

Page 77

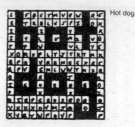

Hot dog

Page 78

Page 79

Page 80

Across: 1. Starboard, 5. Rich, 7. Cord, 8. Groan, 11. Pole, 12. Drum, 13. Petticoat.
Down: 2. Trim, 3. Orchard, 4. Rare, 6. Harvest, 9. Core, 10. Tuba.

Route 2.

Solutions

Page 81

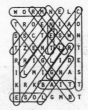

Page 82

1. Bank, 2. Crown, 3. Jester, 4. Wobble, 5. Jealous,
6. Blanket, 7. Nautical.

Page 86

Crab, Lobster, Anemone, Jellyfish, Limpet, Mussel,
Shrimp, Barnacle, Winkle, Whelk, Cockle, Starfish.

Page 83

A and D.

Page 87

Page 84

Page 88

Picture 5.

Page 85

Page 90

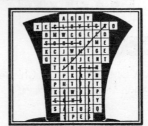

Solutions

Page 91

Path B.

Page 92

Acorn	Grant	Opens
Black	Hover	Plump
Crest	Jaunt	Roars
Drove	Limps	Sport
Event	Maims	Trust
Flash	Never	Vomit

Page 93

Page 94

Lettuce, Cheese, Tomato, Chicken, Cucumber, Mayonnaise, Ham.

Page 95

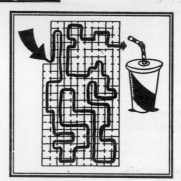

Page 96

Silhouette B.

Page 97   Page 98

Laura is talking to Jenny. They are talking about going to the CINEMA.

Page 99

No. 2.

Page 100

Solutions

Page 112

Across: 1. Brown, 6. Team, 7. Soil, 8. Letter, 12. Danube, 15. Aria, 16. Used, 17. Study.
Down: 2. Roof, 3. Well, 4. Heath, 5. Smart, 9. Ebb, 10. Odour, 11. Anger, 13. East, 14. Bind.

Page 113

Page 114

Page 115

Solutions

Page 101

1. F1, 2. D3, 3. A3, 4. B1, 5. G2, 6.H4,
7. A2, 8. F2, 9. D1, 10. G3, 11. C4.

Page 102

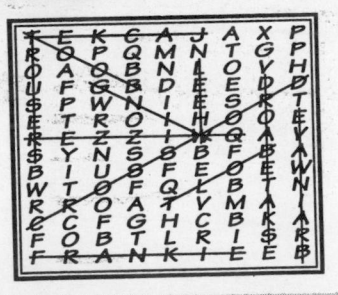

Kneepads, Helmet, Elbowpads.

Page 103

The next letter is Y. They go up in fours.

Regan, Everest, Thyme, Respect,
Ireland, Engineer, Valour, Endure,
Rhine.
The breed of dog is: RETRIEVER.

Page 104

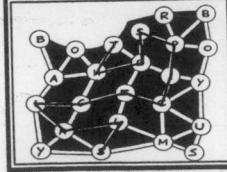

The Spice Girls.

Page 105

No. 3 is the odd one out.

Page 106

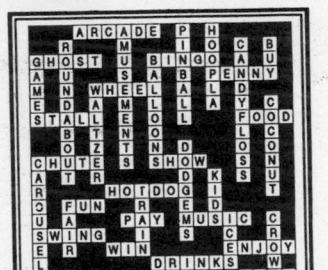

Page 107   Opera.

Page 108

No. 5 is saying 'three', all the
rest are staying 'two'.

Page 109

Foot Boot, Bolt,
Belt, Bell, Ball.

Page 110

1. Vanilla, 2. Strawberry,
3. Banana, 4. Chocolate.

Page 111

1. Red, 2. Blue, 3. Yellow, 4. Brown.

Page 112